SUPER
COLOR & ACTIVITY BOOK

D1497024

nickelodeonjr.tv

**Adventure Bay needs our help!
Let's go, PAW Patrol!**

T

Color the objects that begin with the letter T.

WHICH IS DIFFERENT?

Which picture is different from the others?

A   D

B   E

C   F

Draw a line to connect the matching objects.

Color the fire truck.
Then practice printing the words.

WHICH PATH?

Which path leads Ryder to Zuma?

A
B
C

ANSWER: A

DRAWING

Draw your own badge.

WHICH IS DIFFERENT?

Which picture is different from the others?

A

B

C

ANSWER: A

CHASE IS ON THE CASE!

How many strawberries do you count?

Your Answer:

WHICH IS DIFFERENT?

Which picture is different from the others?

A

B

C

ANSWER: C

Draw a line to connect the matching animals.

Trace the path from Rubble to his bowl.

Draw a line to connect the matching pups.

WHICH IS DIFFERENT?

Which picture is different from the others?

A   B

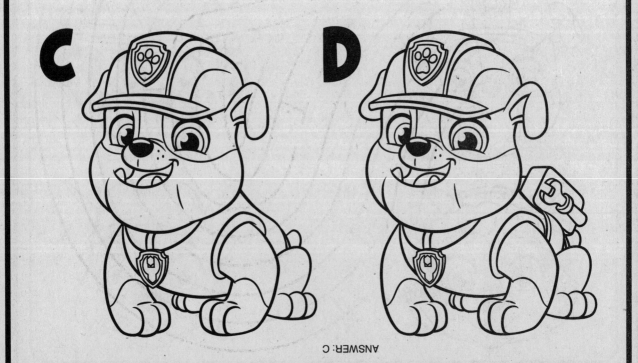

C   D

A-MAZE-ING!

Help Chase take to the sky!

FINISH

START

MISSING PIECE

Which paw print completes the picture?

A

B

C
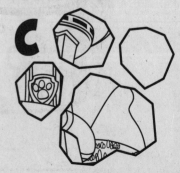

ANSWER: B

WHICH IS DIFFERENT?

Which picture is different from the others?

A

B

C

ANSWER: B

Color Katie.
Then practice printing her name.

KATIE

Color the two objects that rhyme.

Answer: star and car

A-MAZE-ING!

Help Rocky get to the ball.

START

FINISH

DRAWING

Finish the drawing.

Color the number 6s.
How many did you find?

Your Answer:

Answer: 5

FREE TO BE ME!

Circle the beginning sound for each object.

C G Y S

E H D F

N S W E

L B C V

WHICH IS DIFFERENT?

Which picture is different from the others?

A

B

C

I'M ALL EARS AND ALL GEARS!

How many jars of jam do you count?

Your Answer:

Color the two objects that rhyme.

Answer: chair and bear

A-MAZE-ING!

Help Marshall get to his fire engine!

START

FINISH

Color Marshall.
Then match him to his correct shadow.

A

B

C

Your Answer:

Color the number 2s.
How many did you find?

Your Answer:

MARSHALL

DRAWING

Finish the drawing.

Circle the beginning sound for each object.

J I K M   Y P O R

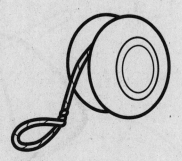

T N B C   R S V E

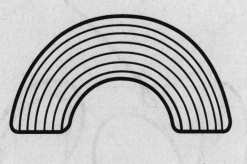

Color the objects that begin with the letter W.

Color Rocky.
Then, practice printing his name.

ROCKY

Draw a line to connect the matching badges.

SHADOW MATCH

Which shadow matches ?

A   **B**   **C**

ANSWER: A

Circle the beginning sound for each object.

H K I S

B M Y J

F D R W

S L G A

Color the horse using the color key below.

Color Key

1 = Pink

2 = Brown

3 = Yellow

4 = Black

Color Zuma.
Then match him to his correct shadow.

A

B

C

Your Answer:

SHADOW MATCH

Which shadow matches ?

A

B

C

How many ice cream cones do you count?

Your Answer:

Color the flowers using the color key below.

Color Key

1 = Red
2 = Yellow
3 = Orange
4 = Pink
5 = Green

WHICH PATH?

Which path leads Marshall to Robo Dog?

A

B

C

A-MAZE-ING!

Help Rubble get to his tools!

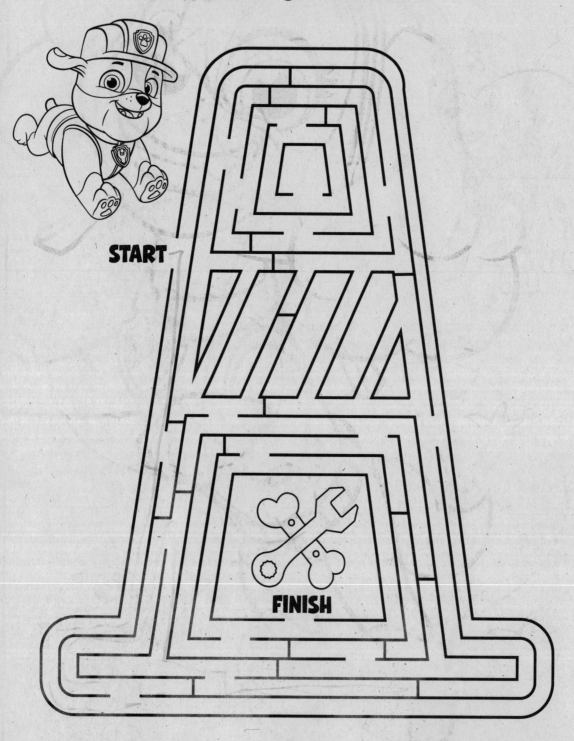

START

FINISH

WHICH IS DIFFERENT?

Which picture is different from the others?

A

B

C

ANSWER: C

DRAWING

Finish the scene.

SHADOW MATCH

Which shadow matches ?

A

B

C

ANSWER: B

¡HOLA, AMIGOS!

DUDE, TOTALLY!

READY TO DIVE IN!

B

Color the objects that begin with the letter B.

How many yo-yos do you count?

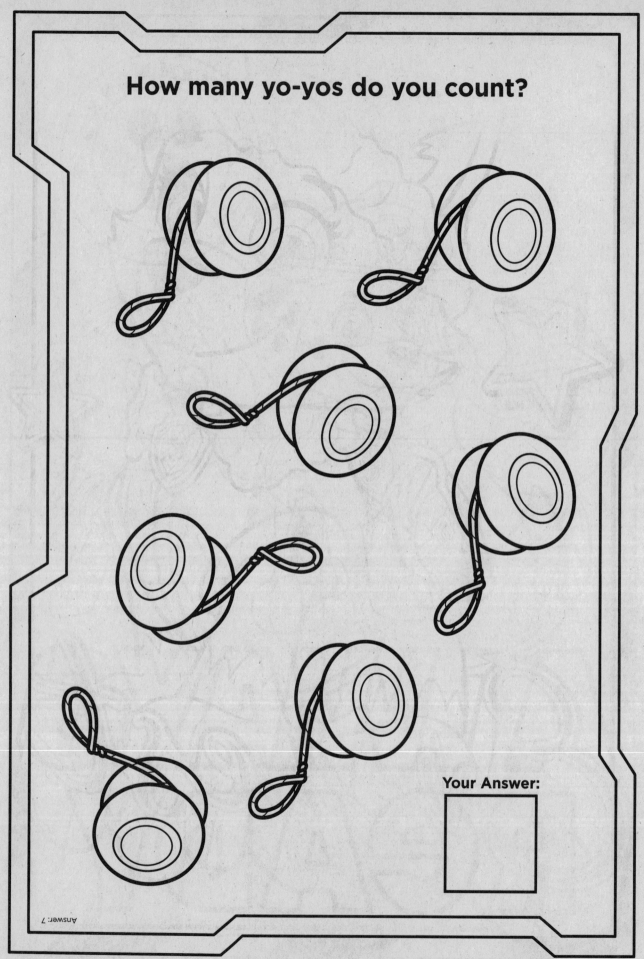

Your Answer:

MISSING PIECE

Which paw print completes the picture?

A **B** **C**

ANSWER: A

Trace the bee's path.

Draw a line to connect the matching objects.

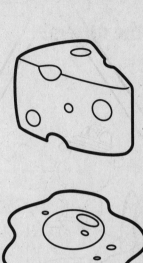

WHICH IS DIFFERENT?

Which picture is different from the others?

Color the two objects that rhyme.

Color the number 7s.
How many did you find?

Your Answer:

Answer: 4

ADVENTURE BAY'S **BRAVEST** 03

How many hats do you count?

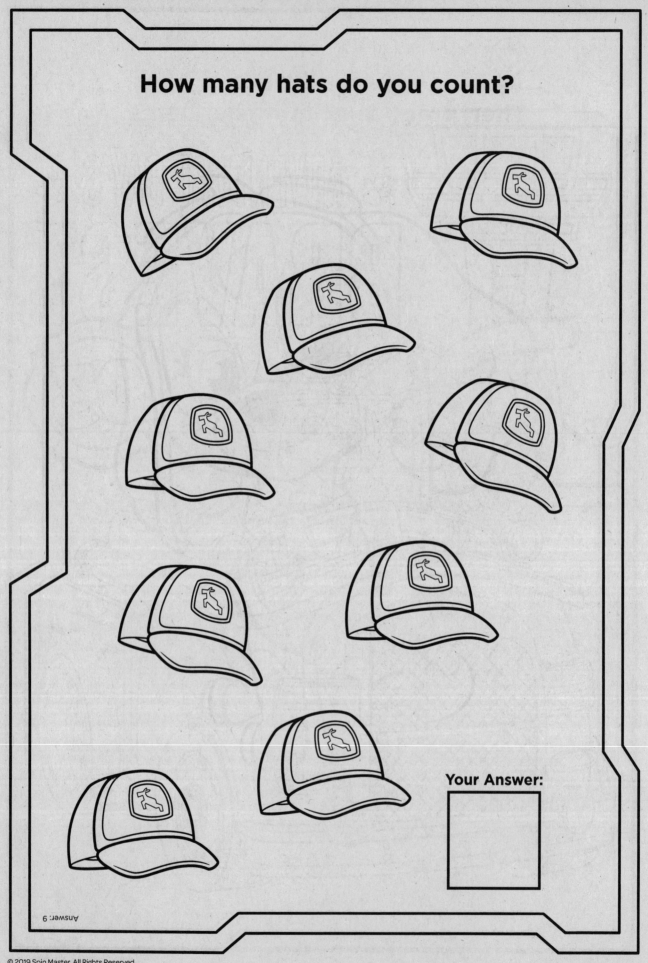

Your Answer:

Color Skye.
Then practice printing her name.

SKYE

A-MAZE-ING!

Help Tracker make his way to the jungle.

FINISH

START

MISSING PIECE

Which paw print completes the picture?

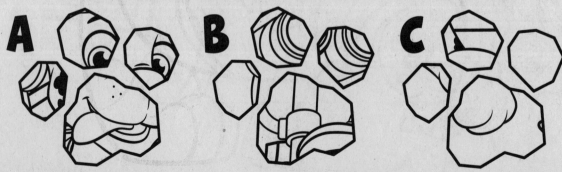

A B C

HERE COMES RUBBLE ON THE DOUBLE!

Color Rubble.
Then practice printing his name.

RUBBLE

BORN BRAVE

Color Zuma.
Then practice printing his name.

ZUMA

DESIGN YOUR OWN
PAW PATROL BADGE!

Write your name here.

WHICH IS DIFFERENT?

Which picture is different from the others?

A

B

C

D

DRAWING

Draw your favorite PAW Patrol pup.

THIS PUP'S GOTTA FLY!

Color the objects that begin with the letter E.

Answer: Egg, Envelope, Elephant

Color the number 4s.
How many did you find?

5 3 2 4

4 3

6 4 1

3 5 1 4

4 2

6 4

Your Answer:

Color Ryder.
Then match him to his correct shadow.

A

B

C

Your Answer:

Trace the butterfly's path.

DRAWING

Finish the drawing.

MISSING PIECE

Which paw print completes the picture?

A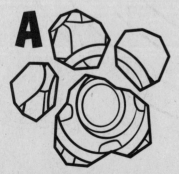

B

C

A-MAZE-ING!

Help Marshall find his sleeping bag.

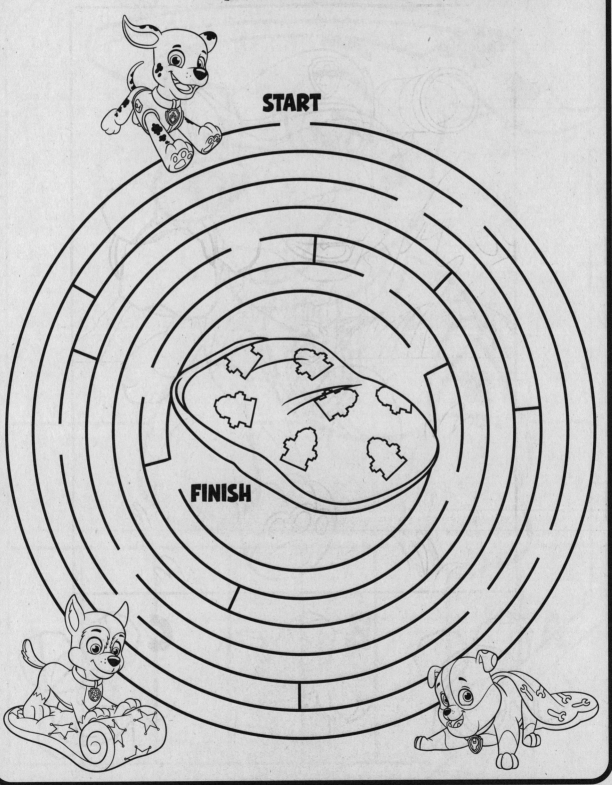

START

FINISH

SHADOW MATCH

Which shadow matches Zuma?

A

B

C

C

Color the objects that begin with the letter C.

TEAM

WHICH IS DIFFERENT?

Which picture is different from the others?

A

D

B

E

C

F

M

Color the objects that begin with the letter M.

Answer: Moon, Microphone, Mushrooms

Color the cow using the color key below.

Color Key

1 = Pink
2 = Brown
3 = Yellow
4 = Black
5 = Red

SHADOW MATCH

Which shadow matches ?

A B C

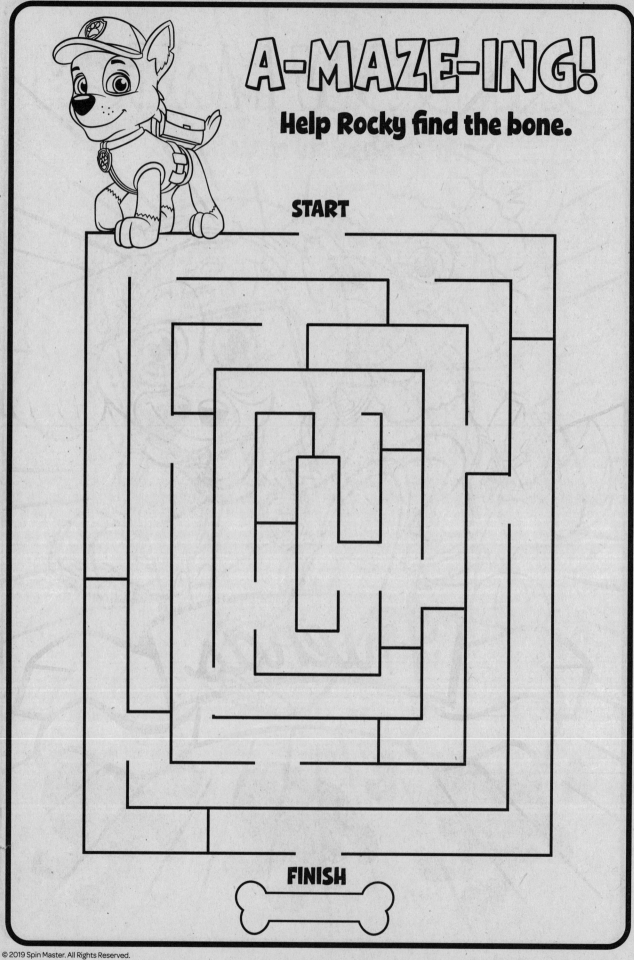

A-MAZE-ING!

Help Rocky find the bone.

START

FINISH

Color the PAW Patrol.
Then practice printing their name.

Color the umbrella using the color key below.

Color Key

1 = Red
2 = Yellow
3 = Orange
4 = Blue
5 = Brown

COUNT IT UP

How many paw prints do you count? Answer: _____

WHICH IS DIFFERENT?

Which Everest is different from the others?

A

B

C

D

TEAMWORK ////ON THE//// DOUBLE

SHADOW MATCH

Which shadow matches ?

A

B

C

GREEN MEANS GO!

WHICH IS DIFFERENT?

Which picture is different from the others?

A

B

C

D

E

F

DRAWING

Finish the drawing.

BADGE MATCH

Match each badge to the right PAW Patrol pup.

1 ___

2 ___

3 ___

4 ___

5 ___

6 ___

A

B

C

D

E

F